Rosie & Jim
Annual 1996

CONTENTS

written by Kjartan Poskitt
illustrated by Helen Prole
designed by John Taggart

A Smelly Smell

1. One day the Ragdoll was going past a farm. "Gosh, what a funny smell!" said Pat, sniffing the air. "Loopy can smell something funny!" said Rosie.

2. "Pooh!" said Jim. "I can smell something funny too!" "Can you smell it, Duck?" asked Rosie. "Quack?" said Duck.

6

3. "There's a big pile of old rubbish going along," said Jim. "It's smelly rubbish!" giggled Rosie.

4. "I'm going to hold my nose to stop the smell going in," said Jim. "So am I," said Rosie.

5. "Are you going to hold your nose, Duck?" asked Rosie. "Where is Duck's nose?" said Jim.

6. "Duck's nose isn't like our noses," said Rosie. "It's on top of Duck's beak," said Jim.

7. "Here's a good place to tie up the Ragdoll," said Pat. "There are some other noses, Jim," said Rosie.

8. "I think I'll draw some pictures of the animals," said Pat. "Look at the pig's nose," said Jim. "He's got a nice pink nose," said Rosie. "Snorty, snort," said the pig.

9. "Here comes the dog," said Jim. "He's got a shiny black nose," said Rosie. "Sniff, sniff," went the dog.

10. "The horse has got a long nose," said Jim. "A long nose is nice to stroke," said Rosie.

11. "Quack, quack!" shouted Duck. "Duck says there's something coming," said Rosie. "I wonder what it is?" said Jim.

12. "Oh, no. It's the smelly rubbish coming!" said Rosie. "Oh, no!" said Jim.

13. "Oh, no!" said Pat. "I can't be sniffing that smell while I'm painting. Where's my scarf?" "What does Loopy want her scarf for?" said Jim.

14. "That's better!" said Pat. "Now I can't smell the smell!"

15. "I don't want to smell the smelly smell, either," said Jim. "Nor do I," said Rosie. "In fact nobody does!" "I have an idea," said Jim.

16. "We'll use these cloths from the old Ragdoll," said Jim.

17. "Now then," said Pat. "It's time to get on with my picture of the animals."

18. "Goodness me, how did that happen?" said Pat. "Nobody can smell the smelly smell now!" giggled Rosie and Jim.

19. Now Pat had a good idea for a new picture. But where's Duck?

All Kinds Of Noses

1. Back on the Ragdoll, Rosie and Jim decided to play a noses game.

2. "What kind of nose have I got?" said Jim. "You've got a nose like Duck," said Rosie.

3. "What kind of nose have I got?" said Rosie. "You've got a nose like a pig," said Jim. "Snorty, snort," giggled Rosie.

4. "What kind of nose have I got?" said Jim. "You've got a nose like a dog," said Rosie. "Sniff, sniff," said Jim.

5. "What kind of nose have I got?" said Rosie. "It's a long nose like the horse," said Jim, and he stroked it.

"Quack, quack!"

6. "Look, Duck is playing the noses game too!" said Jim. "But what kind of nose has Duck got?" said Rosie.

7. "It's a very, very long nose!" said Jim. "Nobody has a nose as long as that," said Rosie. "Quack," said Duck.

8. Just then a big parade came down the road. "Look at all the people!" said Rosie. "And look, there's a big grey elephant!" said Jim. "With a big long nose!"

9. "Why does he have a big long nose like that?" said Rosie. "Let's give him a wave," said Jim.

10. "Look, he's waving back!" said Rosie. "So that's what his big long nose is for!" said Jim.

Noses can be curly,
Noses can be straight,
Noses can be little,
Noses can be great.

Noses help you sniff,
Or help you puff and pant,
And everyone knows
The biggest nose
Is on an elephant.

The Noses Game

Pat has drawn some noses. Can you see whose nose is whose?

"One of those noses looks like yours, Jim."

Is there a nose that looks like yours?

The Smelly Box Game!

Play this with a friend.

Find a box and make some little holes in the top. Find some smelly things like a banana, soap, cheese, flower, and smelly sock.

Put one of the smelly things in the box (don't let your friend see which one). Let your friend sniff the holes and guess what is in the box!

Pat's Train Ride

1. "I'd better hurry," said Pat, "or I'll miss my train."

2. "Look at Loopy putting everything into her bag," said Jim. "Maybe we can help her fill it up," said Rosie.

3. "Here are some carrots and a light," said Rosie. "Here's a pan and a clock," said Jim. "Her bag is nearly full now."

4. "Time to go," said Pat. "Gosh, I can hardly shut my case!" "That's because we helped to fill it," giggled Rosie.

5. "Quack, quack," shouted Duck. "The train is coming!" said Jim. "I'm ready just in time," said Pat.

6. "This case is very heavy!" said Pat. "Because we filled it up so well," said Jim.

7. "Time to wave the flag to make the train set off," said the guard. "But Loopy hasn't got in the train yet!" said Rosie.

8. "Off you go then!" said the guard, waving his flag.
"QUACK, QUACK, QUACK!" shouted Duck, very loudly.
"The train is making a funny noise," said the driver.

9. "I can't set off while the train is making that noise!" said the driver.
"Loopy has got on the train now!" said Rosie. "Try again," said the
guard. "The train has stopped making the funny noise now," said
the driver. "Off we go then!" "Bye bye, Loopy," said Rosie and Jim.

Big Jelly Station

1. "We could make a train," said Jim. "Let's make lots of trucks, too," said Rosie.

2. "This could be Big Jelly station," said Rosie. "The train could bring you something!" said Jim.

3. "What does Big Jelly station need?" said Jim. "A big jelly needs big spoons!" said Rosie.

4. "It might need some jelly bowls, too," said Rosie. "I'll get some."

5. "And special jelly napkins," said Rosie, "and a custard jug."

6. "Jim, where are you?" said Rosie.

7. "Help!" said Jim.

8. "Maybe it would be easier if Big Jelly station came over to the train," said Rosie. "Toot, toot! Here comes the station!" agreed Jim.

22

Stations

23

Train Tracks

One sunny day, Rosie and Jim and Duck were going for a walk when they heard a big CRASH!

"Whatever can that be?" asked Rosie. Next they heard a loud TOOT, TOOT!

"I don't know," said Jim.

"Quack," said Duck, and pointed behind some bushes. Rosie and Jim went to see what Duck had found.

"It's a train!" they said.

"What are you doing there?" said Jim.

"I'm taking the tomato sauce to Sausage Sandwich station," said the train, "but I've got lost."

"We'll help you find Sausage Sandwich station," said Rosie.

"Thank you," said the train.

Rosie and Jim looked everywhere, but they couldn't see a station. Just then Duck did a big, "Quack!"

"Duck has found some iron lines on the ground," said Rosie.

"They are very long and go on forever," said Jim.

"Those are my train tracks!" said the train. "They show me where I have to go!" Rosie and Jim and Duck gave the train a big push back on to the train tracks.

"Thank you!" said the train. "Why don't you climb on and I'll give you all a ride to Sausage Sandwich station!"

"Yes, please!" said Rosie and Jim. "TOOT, TOOT!" went the train. "QUACK! QUACK!" went Duck and off they all went.

Footprints

1. One day Pat was sitting in the Ragdoll when there was a BANG and a SPLOSH! "What was that?" said Pat. "It came from outside. I'd better go and look."

2. "QUACK, QUACK!" shouted Duck. "Listen!" said Jim. "Duck knows what it was!"

3. "Oh, dear!" said Pat. "Somebody's knocked over one of my pots of paint!"

4. "Did you knock the paint over, Duck?" said Jim. "Quack," said Duck. "Then who could it be?" said Rosie.

5. "I'd better get a cloth and start cleaning up," said Pat.

6. "Look, there are some painty marks," said Jim. "I wonder where they go!" "Let's follow them and see," said Rosie.

7. "Here they are!" said Rosie. "They go over here," said Jim.

8. "They go through the door!" said Rosie.

9. "Where are they now?" said Jim. "I can't see them," said Rosie. Can you help Rosie and Jim? Can you see the marks?

10. "The painty marks go outside again," said Jim. "They go over to Duck," said Rosie.

11. "Quack!" said Duck. "Look, there's a little kitten!" said Rosie. "There are marks all around him," said Jim.

12. "He's got Loopy's paint on his feet!" said Rosie. "And when he walks, he makes the painty marks!" said Jim.

The old Ragdoll is very neat.
The Ragdoll is so clean.

But SPLISH, SPLOSH,
Went the messy feet.
Can you see where they've been?

13. "Maybe we could help Pat and clean up the painty foot marks," said Rosie. "Yes," said Jim. "They are only little marks. They won't take very long."

14. "Where did my cleaning cloth go?" said Pat. Can you see where it is?

15. "Quack, quack!" said Duck. "What has Duck seen now?" said Jim.

16. "Look, there are a lot more painty marks!" said Rosie.

17. "These are big painty marks!" said Jim. "Who made them?" "Let's follow them and see," said Rosie.

"QUACK, QUACK!"

18. "Look, Rosie!" said Jim. "Oh dear, Jim!" said Rosie.

19. "It was us that did the big painty marks!" said Jim. "We'd better start cleaning up straight away!" said Rosie.

20. "There's one job we should do first," said Jim. "What's that?" asked Rosie.

21. "Take off our painty shoes!" laughed Jim.

SPLISH! SPLOSH! the kitten made, a mess along the floor. SPLOSH! SPLASH! Rosie and Jim made the mess even more.

Making Footprints

1. "Look at these old shoes, Rosie," said Jim. "We could use them to make footprints," said Rosie.

2. "I've put a painty footprint on this paper, Rosie," said Jim.

3. "He needs some squiggles," said Rosie. "Then he can be a footprint man."

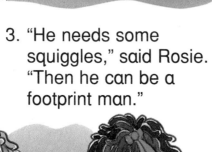

4. "I've got paint all over my hand," said Rosie.

5. "Put your painty hand over his head," said Jim.

6. "Look! He's got Rosie's hand hair now!" laughed Jim.

7. "I'm going to make lots more footprint men!" said Jim. "I'm going to make a very special footprint," said Rosie. Can you see who Rosie has made?

Duck makes different footprints.
So does the horse and the dog.
Can you see where they have been?

And where has Pat been?

Stepping Stones

1. "Look at the old watermill," said Pat. "That would be a good place to paint a picture."

2. "How will Loopy get over there?" said Jim. "I can't see a bridge," agreed Rosie.

3. "Off I go," said Pat. "Loopy's going to fall in the water!" giggled Jim.

4. "Look. Loopy is walking on the water!" said Rosie. "It must be magic," said Jim.

5. "Look, Jim. There's something down there," said Rosie. "It looks like big stones." " We could walk on the stones, too!" said Jim. "Be careful!" warned Rosie.

6. "It's easy!" shouted Jim. "Look at me!" "Watch where you put your feet, Jim!" shouted Rosie.

7. SPLOSH! "You should have looked where you were going!" laughed Rosie.

8. "There should be lots more stones," said Jim. "Let's find some!' said Rosie.

9. "Here's a good stone. I'll put it in this gap," said Rosie.

10. "Quack, quack!" shouted Duck.

11. "There, that's the last gap filled," said Jim. "People won't step in the stream now!" "People can walk across here now," said Jim. "And nobody will ever get their feet wet again!" said Rosie.

12. "Loopy's coming back!" said Jim. "These stepping stones are much better," said Pat.

13. "Look, Jim. All our stones have stopped the stream!" said Rosie.

14. "Oh, no!" shouted Rosie. "The stream has pushed our stones over!"

15. "At last, here we are back on the good old Ragdoll," said Jim. "Yes," said Rosie. "This is the best way to go across water!"

River Blue

"River Blue is far too wide,
for me to reach the other side!"

"I only have two stones to help me get across," said Jim. "How am I going to get over to see you, Rosie?"
"I don't know," said Rosie. "I only have two stones to help me get across, so how can I get over to see you?"

"My two stones hardly let me get halfway across," said Jim.
"My two stones hardly let me get halfway across to you," said Rosie.
"Look!"

"I know," said Jim. "Why don't we meet halfway?"

"I'll move my stones along to you, and you move yours along to me."
"There!" said Rosie. "Four stones in a line! We can cross River Blue after all!"

The Bridge Stones

One day Rosie and Jim and Duck were walking along by the side of a stream when they heard a funny noise.

"What's making that funny noise?" asked Rosie.

"We are!"

Rosie and Jim and Duck looked down. They saw a pile of big old stones. "Who are you?" asked Jim.

"We're the bridge stones," said the stones. "We used to hold the bridge up."

"But I can't see a bridge," said Rosie.

"That's because it's gone," wailed the stones.

"Oh, dear," said Jim. "But why are you unhappy?"

43

"Because we're bridge stones," said the stones. "We like helping people get over the stream, but we can't now. We haven't got a bridge to hold up."

"Maybe you can help people across the stream without a bridge," said Jim.

"How can we do that?" asked the stones.

"We can show you how to be stepping stones," said Rosie. "Would you like that?"

"Oh, yes, please," said the stones. One by one, Rosie and Jim picked up the stones and dropped them across the stream. "There!" said Jim. "People can step across you now. Watch us!" Rosie and Jim and Duck stepped across the stones to the other side.

"We helped you to get across!" said the bridge stones proudly.

"And a very good job you did of it too!" laughed Rosie and Jim.

"Quack!" said Duck.

Stepping Stones with Rosie and Jim

This puddle has lots of pretty stepping stones.

Jim steps on the red stones.
Rosie steps on the yellow stones.
Duck steps on the blue stones.
Pat steps on the green stones.

Can you see where each one is going to go?

45

Pat's Lost Earring

1. "Oh, dear," said Pat. "Where has my other earring gone?"
"What's Loopy-Lobes looking for?" asked Rosie.
"She's looking for one of her loops that goes in her ears," said Jim. "It goes in her lobes," said Rosie.

2. "It's not in here..." said Pat.

3. "...or under here..."

4. "...or in here..."

5. "...or here!"

6. "Where is the other one like this one?" said Pat. "But she's got one of her loops in her hand!" said Rosie.

7. "I think she needs two loops," said Jim, "because she's got two ears."

8. "Loopy-Lobes won't be Loopy without her loopy things," said Jim. "She'll just be Lobes," said Rosie.

9. "Maybe we could help her find her loop," said Rosie. "We could look outside for it."

10. "But what does it look like?" said Jim.
"Like this," said Rosie. "Right," said Jim. "Let's get looking."

11. "It isn't under here," said Rosie. "It isn't on here," said Jim.

12. "Do you think this is it?" said Jim. "I don't think so," said Rosie.

13. "Maybe she could fix it on her ear anyway," said Jim. "Does it look pretty?" "I don't think so, Jim. What do you think, Duck?" said Rosie.

14. "Maybe Duck can help," said Jim. "Yes, Duck," said Rosie. "Loopy is looking for one of her Loops, just like this one. Have you seen it?"

15. "Duck says this is Loopy's lost loop," said Jim. "And we had it all the time!" "Silly us!" giggled Rosie.

16. "Quack!" said Duck. "There's Loopy still looking," said Jim.

Loopy-Lobes looks for her loop,
She's looking high and low.
Where is Loopy-Lobe's loop?
Jim and Rosie know.

17. "Oh, where can my earring have got to?" said Pat. "Drop it down for her," whispered Rosie.

18. PLUNK! "Gosh!" gasped Pat. "There it is! But where did it come from?"

19. "Shhh, Jim!" said Rosie. "I'm glad Loopy's happy now " whispered Jim.

20. "I still think this would be a good loop for Loopy-Lobes," giggled Jim.

Let's Make Some Lobey Loops

1. "Don't you like these lobey loops?" asked Jim. "Oh Jim, you do look silly!" giggled Rosie.

2. "What else can we make loops from?" said Rosie. "How about these leaves?" said Jim.

3. "Maybe Duck would like those ones," said Rosie. "Quack!" said Duck.

4. "Here are some good ones for you, Rosie," said Jim. "You like bananas, don't you?"

5. "You need some too, Jim," said Rosie. "I know what you like. You like sausages, don't you?"

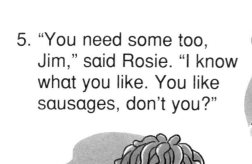

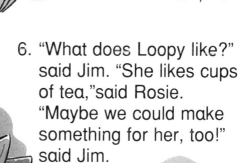

6. "What does Loopy like?" said Jim. "She likes cups of tea,"said Rosie. "Maybe we could make something for her, too!" said Jim.

7. "Quack!" said Duck. "Thank you, Duck!" said Jim. "Loopy's coming!" said Rosie "We must be very still!"

8. "Goodness me," said Pat. "What have we here?" "These look like fun!" said Pat. "She likes them!" whispered Jim. "I knew she would," said Rosie. "I hope she wears them all day!"

'Ere, Ear!

One sunny day, Rosie and Jim and Duck were out walking when they found a big earring.

"Hello," said Rosie and Jim.

"Hello," said the earring.

"What are you doing out here all alone," said Rosie.

"I'm lost!" said the earring.

"We'll find out where you should be," said Jim.

Rosie and Jim went off with the earring and found a big nose sniffing. "Is this your earring?" said Rosie.

"No," said the nose. "I don't have an earring. I have a handkerchief. Ah...tishoo!"

Next they saw a big mouth yawning. "Is this your earring?" said Jim.

"No," said the mouth. "I don't have an earring. I have a lipstick."

Next they saw a big foot. "Is this your earring?" said Rosie.

"No," said the big foot. "I don't have an earring. I have a smart sock to put on."

"Oh, dear," said Rosie. "We don't know whose earring you are."

"He's my earring!" said a voice. They all turned round and saw...a great big ear! "There you are," said the ear.

"Yes, 'ere I am," said the earring. "Where's my sister?"

"Over 'ere," came a voice.

Rosie and Jim saw another big ear with another earring. "Thank you for looking after my earring," said the first ear. "But don't you have an earring of your own?"

"Quack!" said Duck.

"No," said Rosie and Jim. "We have a Duck."

Matching the Earrings Game

Oh, dear! Rosie has knocked over Pat's box of earrings. Can you help Jim put the earrings together in matching pairs?

Draw a line between the earrings that match. The first line has already been drawn for you.

Lucky Dip!

Pick some of your favourite foods, such as a clean carrot, a biscuit or a banana.
Draw a picture of each one.

Put all the pictures in an old box.

Pull out a picture and then eat that food first!

57

Old King Duck

Old King Cole was a merry old soul,
and a merry old soul was he.
He called for his pipe
and he called for his drum,
and he called for his fiddlers three.

"Quack, quack, quack."

Old King Duck was a merry old Duck,
with a red cloak on his back.
He called for Rosie
and he called for Jim,
and then said, "Quack, quack, quack."

Where Is...?

Where is Rosie?
Where is Jim?
I haven't seen her
I haven't seen him.

Never mind,
they'll soon come back
when Duck gives a
great big "QUACK."

"Quack."

Peep-bo Back

Can you play peep-bo back through the book to find
these things on the pages?
See what colours they are, then colour in the squares.

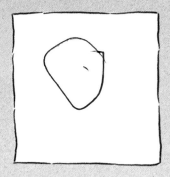

page 8 the dog's nose

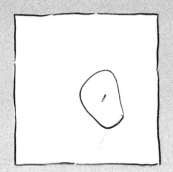

page 19 Pat's suitcase

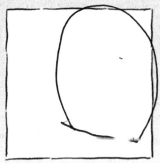

page 27 the painty marks

page 59 Old King Duck's cloak

Answers

page 8 the dog's nose is black; page 19 Pat's suitcase is brown.
page 27 the painty marks are blue; page 59 Duck's cloak is red.

1. Rosie and Jim, Rosie and Jim
Chugging along on the old Ragdoll.

2. Rosie and Jim, Rosie and Jim
And Pat...she steers the boat.

3. We go to play and have a look
With Rosie's bag and Jim's drawing book.

4. The world drifts by the window frame
And Rosie and Jim we play our games.

5. Rosie and Jim, Rosie and Jim
Finding stories every day.

6. Rosie and Jim, Rosie and Jim
And Pat...she colours them in.